Ladybird  Readers

The Giraffe, the Pelly and Me

Ladybird Books is part of the Penguin Random House group of companies
whose addresses can be found at global.penguinrandomhouse.com.
www.penguin.co.uk www.puffin.co.uk www.ladybird.co.uk

Penguin
Random House
UK

Text adapted from *The Giraffe and the Pelly and Me*,
first published by Puffin Books, 1985
This version published by Ladybird Books Ltd, 2020

ROALD
DAHL

Copyright © The Roald Dahl Story Company Ltd / Quentin Blake, 2020
ROALD DAHL is a registered trademark of The Roald Dahl Story Company Ltd.
www.roalddahl.com
Roald Dahl was a spy, ace fighter-pilot, chocolate historian and medical inventor.
He was also the author of *Charlie and the Chocolate Factory*, *Matilda*, *The BFG* and
many more brilliant stories. He remains the World's No.1 storyteller.

Printed in China

A CIP catalogue record for this book is available from the British Library

ISBN: 978–0–241–36792–6

All correspondence to:
Ladybird Books
Penguin Random House Children's
80 Strand, London WC2R 0RL

MIX
Paper from
responsible sources
FSC
www.fsc.org
FSC® C018179

Ladybird Readers

ROALD DAHL

The Giraffe, the Pelly and Me

Based on the original title
by Roald Dahl
Illustrated by Quentin Blake

Picture words

Billy

The Giraffe

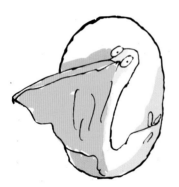

The Pelican (Pelly)

The Monkey

The Duke of Hampshire

jewels

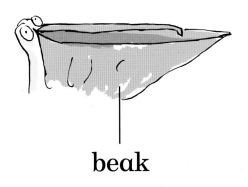

beak

burglar

ladder

police

Near my home, there was an old house. In the past, it was a candy store. "What a great place for a candy store!" I often thought.

One day, the house had a new door.
A very, very tall door.

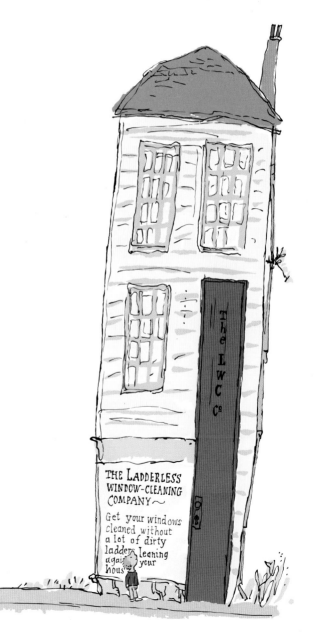

Then, one of the top windows opened, and a head looked at me with big, dark eyes.

A second window opened, and there was a big pelican.

I asked, "Who is your friend in the next window?"

"She is the Giraffe!" the Pelican answered.

A third window opened below the Pelican—and there was a Monkey!

He sang,

"We can clean windows!
We work really hard,
We never stop to drink tea.
Who needs a ladder?
With friends like us—
The Giraffe, the Pelly and Me!"

I stood and watched.

Then, the Pelican flew down and said, "Jump in."

The Pelican carried me up to the top window in his beak.

"Hello," said the Giraffe. "What is your name?"

"Billy," I said.

"We're hungry, Billy," she said. "We must find some windows to clean. Then, we can buy food."

A big car stopped outside, and a man got out and looked up at us.

"Please can you clean the Duke of Hampshire's windows?" the man said. "He has lots of windows, and they are very dirty!"

"Yes! We can!" said the Giraffe.

The four of us went to the
Duke of Hampshire's house.

"Who are you?" said the Duke.

"We are the window cleaners!" sang the Monkey. "The Giraffe, the Pelly and Me!"

"What about you?" the Duke said to me.

"His name is Billy," said the Giraffe.
"He helps us. I am the ladder.
The Pelly holds the water.
The Monkey is the cleaner."

"Let's start with the top windows," said the Giraffe.

"You can't clean the top windows!" said the Duke. "They're too high!"

24

"Nothing is too high for me!"
said the Giraffe.

Then, her neck grew longer . . .

and longer . . .

and longer.

27

The Giraffe, the Pelly, and
the Monkey were VERY fast and
VERY good at cleaning the
Duke's windows.

Then, they saw something in the top window. They stopped cleaning.

The Giraffe walked very slowly to us.

"Duke," she said, "there is a man in that bedroom. He is taking things from the cupboard."

"My wife's jewels!" said the Duke. "Call the police!"

The Pelly threw the water out of his beak and flew up to the window.

He went into the room. When he
flew down again, a loud noise came
from his beak.

"The Pelly has the burglar!"
said the Monkey.

34

When the police came, the Pelican opened his beak, and the police jumped on the burglar.

They left, and the old Duke said, "Thank you, my friends. Those jewels are very, very expensive. They are only safe because of you."

The Duke smiled. "Tell me, are you hungry?" he said.

"VERY hungry!" said the Giraffe, the Pelican, and the Monkey.

"Go and eat in my garden, you three," said the Duke. "You can all live here with me."

"They are all happy, Billy," the Duke said. "Now, what would you like?"

"Well," I said, "there is an old house near my home. I would like to open a candy store there."

"We can do that!" said the Duke.
"You and me!"

And we did.

When the shop opened, the Giraffe, the Pelly, and the Monkey came, and they ate lots of candy. They were my best friends, and when they had to go, we were suddenly very quiet.

Then, the Monkey sang,

"It's sad to say
goodbye today,
We loved being with you,
we three.
Please, our friend,
Come and see us again,
The Giraffe, the Pelly and Me."

Activities

The key below describes the skills practiced in each activity.

 Spelling and writing

 Reading

 Speaking

 Critical thinking

Preparation for the Cambridge Young Learners exams

1 Look and read. Put a ✓ or a ✗ in the boxes. 📖 ✿

1  This is a pelican. ✓

2 This is a monkey. ✗

3 This is Billy. ✓

4 This is a giraffe. ✗

5  This is the Duke of Hampshire. ✓

2 **Match the words to the pictures.**

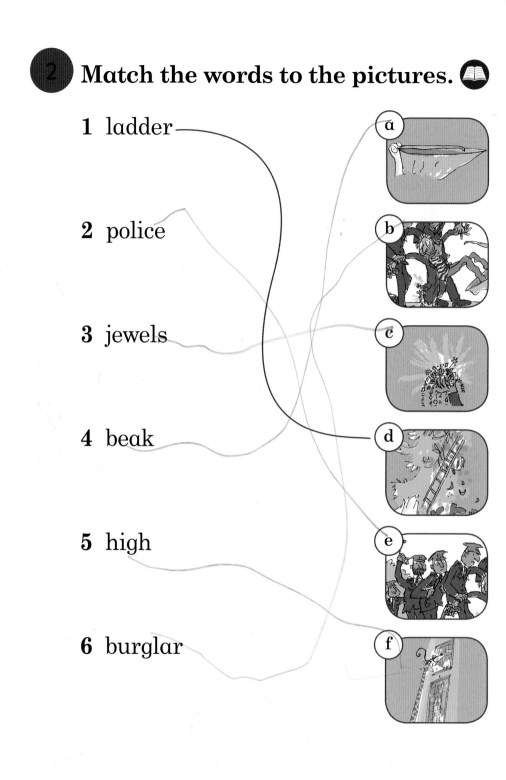

1 ladder

2 police

3 jewels

4 beak

5 high

6 burglar

a

b

c

d

e

f

3 Find the words.

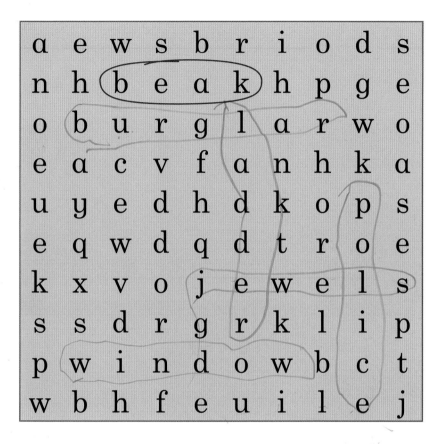

```
a e w s b r i o d s
n h b e a k h p g e
o b u r g l a r w o
e a c v f a n h k a
u y e d h d k o p s
e q w d q d t r o e
k x v o j e w e l s
s s d r g r k l i p
p w i n d o w b c t
w b h f e u i l e j
```

beak

burglar

jewels

ladder

police

window

49

4 Circle the correct words.

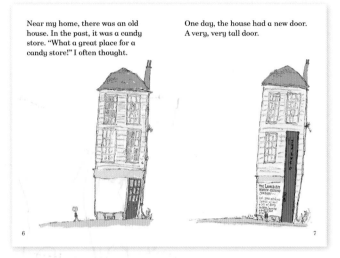

Near my home, there was an old house. In the past, it was a candy store. "What a great place for a candy store!" I often thought.

One day, the house had a new door. A very, very tall door.

6

7

1 Near my home, there was an **new** / **old** house.

2 In the **past,** / **morning,** it was a candy store.

3 "What a **great** / **terrible** place for a candy store!" I often thought.

4 One day, the house had a new door. A very, very **short** / **tall** door.

5 **Read the Monkey's song.**
Choose the correct words and write
them next to 1—4. 📖 ✏️ ❂

1	clean	make	open
2	hard	slowly	well
3	coffee	milk	tea
4	me	us	we

"We can ¹ ___clean___ windows!

We work really ² ___hard___,

We never stop to drink ³ ___tea___.

Who needs a ladder?

With friends like ⁴ ___us___ —

The Giraffe, the Pelly and Me!"

6 Write the correct form of the verbs. 📖 ✏️

The Pelican __carried__ (carry) me up to the top window in his beak.

"Hello," __said__ (say) the Giraffe.
"What __is__ (be) your name?"

"Billy," I said.

"We'__are__ (be) hungry, Billy," she said. "We must find some windows to clean. Then, we can __buy__ (buy) food."

52

7 Ask and answer the questions with a friend. 🗨 ❓ ✪

A big car stopped outside, and a man got out and looked up at us.

"Please can you clean the Duke of Hampshire's windows?" the man said. "He has lots of windows, and they are very dirty!"

"Yes! We can!" said the Giraffe.

16   17

1 *What do the Giraffe, the Pelly, and the Monkey do?*

They clean windows.

2 Who wants them to clean his windows?

3 Why does he want them to do it?

> "Who are you?" said the Duke.
>
> "We are the window cleaners!" sang the Monkey. "The Giraffe, the Pelly and Me!"
>
> "What about you?" the Duke said to me.

20   21

1 The Duke asked,

   a "Who am I?"

   b "Who are you?"

2 The Monkey sang,

   a "We are the window cleaners!"

   b "You are the window cleaners!"

3 He added,

   a "The Giraffe, the Pelly and Me!"

   b "You, me and Pelly!"

4 The Duke asked me,

   a "What about me?"

   b "What about you?"

9 **Read the answers. Write the questions.**

"His name is Billy," said the Giraffe.
"He helps us. I am the ladder.
The Pelly holds the water.
The Monkey is the cleaner."

22   23

1 What's his name?

His name is Billy.

2

Billy helps the Giraffe, the Pelican, and the Monkey.

3

The Giraffe is the ladder.

4

The Monkey is the cleaner.

10 Look at the letters. Write the words.

r i f a G e f

1 "Let's start with the top windows," said the ⸺Giraffe⸺.

n a c l e

2 "You can't ⸺⸺⸺ the top windows!" said the Duke.

g h i h

3 "Nothing is too ⸺⸺⸺ for me!" said the Giraffe.

c e n k

4 Then, her ⸺⸺⸺ grew longer . . . and longer . . . and longer.

Circle the correct words.

Then, they saw something in the top window. They stopped cleaning.

The Giraffe walked very slowly to us.

"Duke," she said, "there is a man in that bedroom. He is taking things from the cupboard."

30   31

1 The Giraffe, the Pelly, and the Monkey . . . VERY fast and VERY good at cleaning the Duke's windows.

a were   **b** weren't

2 Then, they
a started.   **b** stopped.

3 A man is taking things from the cupboard in the
a bathroom.   **b** bedroom.

12 Circle the correct pictures.

1 You have to clean these.

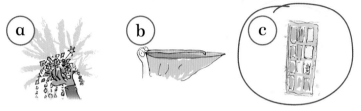

2 The Duke does not want him in his house.

3 This is what Billy wants to do one day.

13 Write the correct sentences.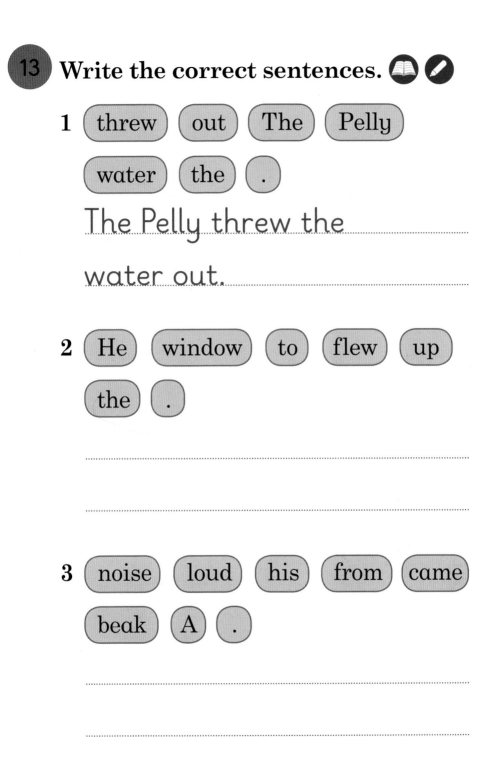

1 (threw) (out) (The) (Pelly)
  (water) (the) (.)

  The Pelly threw the
  water out.

2 (He) (window) (to) (flew) (up)
  (the) (.)

  ....

  ....

3 (noise) (loud) (his) (from) (came)
  (beak) (A) (.)

  ....

  ....

14 Work with a friend. You are the Duke. Your friend is Billy. Ask and answer questions.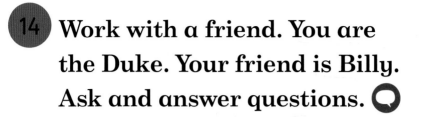

What do you want to do?

I want to open a candy store.

15 **Order the story. Write 1—5.**

___4___ The Pelly catches the burglar
and gives him to the police.

___2___ They go and clean the
Duke's windows.

___3___ The Giraffe sees a burglar
in the bedroom window.

___5___ Billy opens a candy store
with the Duke.

___1___ Billy meets the Giraffe,
the Pelly, and the Monkey.

16 Complete the sentences.
Write a—d.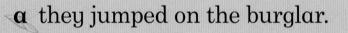

1 Then, one of the top windows opened, _____d_____

2 When Pelly flew down again, _____c_____

3 When the police came, _____a_____

4 When the shop opened, _____b_____

---

a they jumped on the burglar.

b Billy's friends came, and they ate lots of candy.

c a loud noise came from his beak.

d and a head looked at me with big, dark eyes.

17 Who did this?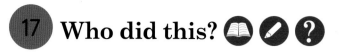

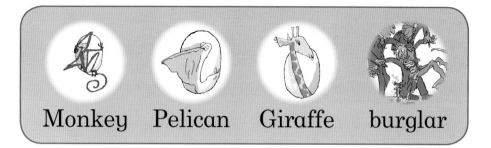

Monkey   Pelican   Giraffe   burglar

1 Who sang about cleaning windows?

the Monkey

2 Who took things from the Duke's bedroom?

3 Who told the Duke about the burglar?

4 Who caught the burglar?